M.I.9 AGENT
SECRET AGENT NAME

- -

AGE -

SPY SKILL - - - - - - - - - - - - - - -

0011005800118650O-5

PLACE
YOUR
PHOTO
HERE

M.I.HIGH

SCHOOL + SPY = M.I.HIGH

ANNUAL 2012

M.I.9

SECRET SERVICE

EGMONT

We bring stories to life

First published in Great Britain 2011 by Egmont UK Limited
239 Kensington High Street, London W8 6SA
Written by Jenny Bak. Designed by Andrea Pollock.
© Kudos Film and Television Ltd. 2011

ISBN 978 1 4052 5972 9
1 3 5 7 9 10 8 6 4 2
Printed in Italy

CONTENTS

M.I. HIGH

The 21st century faces a new kind of threat. Old-school spies have had their day, and M.I.9 must create a new breed of skilled undercover agent.

Hidden in a place no villain will think to look ...
Welcome to M.I. High.

COULD YOU BE A SECRET SPY FOR M.I. HIGH?

Complete this mindboggling mission to be the team's newest recruit!

Pendrix, the pernicious puzzle-maker, has dognapped the Queen's corgis and is holding them in a hidden location – your assignment is to find them!

Your spy pod has detected 16 words in this annual that form a clue to Pendrix's pesky puzzler. Find all 16 words, write the first letters in the spaces below, then use The Encrypter on page 47 to decrypt them with the start code AP. If you've done it right, this will reveal the pooches' prison. Turn to page 68 to check if your mission was a success!

Deep beneath the classrooms of St Hope's High School lies the headquarters of M.I. High – M.I.9's special division of teen spies. Its mission is to protect Britain's national security from danger, particularly the evil schemes of the Grand Master and his Secret Kriminal Underground League.

The M.I. High programme began with three St Hope's students who possessed all the qualities of ace spies – intelligence, courage and loyalty. Daisy, Blane and Rose were expertly trained by Agent Lenny Bicknall and went on to successfully complete many covert missions. Lenny, Blane and Daisy were later chosen to head up a new, international spy network and thus retired from M.I. High duties.

M.I.9 agent Frank London was brought in to train and supervise the next round of teen agents, Rose and new recruits Oscar and Carrie. Through tough missions and trying times, they have grown into a close-knit, unbeatable team.

But with evil villains – old and new – constantly threatening Britain's safety, the M.I. High agents will always be there to help M.I.9 save the country from danger ... and still get their homework in on time!

AGENT PROFILE

CONFIDENTIAL

FRANK LONDON

AGE: Unknown

PROFILE: Supervising agent for M.I. High, tasked with training and supporting the teen spies. Among other duties, Frank briefs them on missions, supplies them with necessary spy tech and information, and advises on action plans. In the course of this assignment, London has formed a close bond with his agents, vowing to protect them at all costs. He has previously defied orders from Chief Agent Stark to apprehend Rose, Carrie and Oscar, and instead helped them remain fugitives until they were proven innocent!

Operates under deep cover as a cheeky caretaker at St Hope's School.

STRENGTH: Scientific background specialising in advanced technology. His awesome gadgets can do anything, from revealing criminal disguises to playing ultrasonic music that stops missiles.

WEAKNESS: His jokes are so cheesy that they're almost deadly weapons themselves.

TOP SECRET TIP: Frank's cousin Carlton was exposed as the evil mastermind The Octopus! When he kidnapped the three M.I.High spies, Frank saved the day by inventing an underwater communicator.

CONTACT DETAILS:

PASSWORD PROTECTED

DENIED
****

ENTER

HEADQUARTERS

DOSSIER LEVEL: CLASSIFIED

Located 230 feet below St Hope's High School, HQ is the nerve centre of M.I. High activity. Here, Frank briefs Carrie, Oscar and Rose on their newest assignments and creates the cool gadgets that help them get the job done. Fitted with superfast computers linked directly to M.I.9, HQ allows the agents to carefully research and plan their dangerous missions.

The secret entrance is hidden in the caretaker's store-room, and can only be accessed with an authorised fingerprint scan. From there, the spies travel deep underground via a high-speed lift that also transforms their school uniforms into sleek spy gear.

TOP SECRET TIP:

Each person has a unique fingerprint. Often, criminals are identified when their fingerprints at the crime scene are matched to the ones in the law-enforcement databases. Computers can scan through 70,000 prints per second to identify a match!

These are three types of fingerprint patterns:

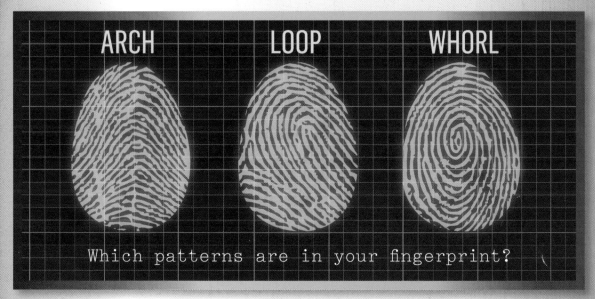

ARCH   LOOP   WHORL

Which patterns are in your fingerprint?

Test your forensic spy skills by drawing lines to match up these pairs of suspects' fingerprints.

Answers: A–K, B–E, C–L, D–I, F–G, H–J.

AGENT PROFILE

CONFIDENTIAL

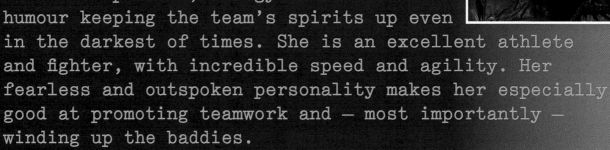

CARRIE STEWART

AGE: 16

PROFILE: Carrie is the heart of M.I. High, with her optimism, energy and sense of humour keeping the team's spirits up even in the darkest of times. She is an excellent athlete and fighter, with incredible speed and agility. Her fearless and outspoken personality makes her especially good at promoting teamwork and — most importantly — winding up the baddies.

STRENGTH: Superior fitness level and highly trained in gymnastics and all forms of hand-to-hand combat. Good knowledge of UK geography gained from travelling to national gymnastics competitions.

M.I.9 AGENT

FEMALE
SURNAME: STEWART
EYES: BROWN
HAIR: BLACK

CARRIE

101111010010011O-0

WEAKNESS: Carrie is terrified of ghosts! She once panicked when she thought a ghost was haunting St Hope's, but it turned out to be a deadly ninja invasion. Luckily, Carrie conquered her fears — and the ninja, too!

TOP SECRET TIP: Carrie's hope and positivity was a critical asset in overcoming the devastating effects of the Despair Bomb, which would have destroyed the world with total misery!

St Hope's High School

Carrie Stewart

Age: 16

Year: 11

Form Teacher: Mr Flatley

046436

Carrie's pencil communicator is blinking – Frank is summoning her!
Lead her through the maze of school corridors to HQ. Be sure
to avoid Mr Flatley and Mrs King or she'll be sent back to class!

START

FINISH

SPY-Q TEASERS

Try these secret agent riddles on your mates!

Q Who do spies call when they make a mess?

A Cleaning agents.

Q What invention allows spies to walk through walls?

A Doors.

Q Why didn't the spy work on cloudy days?

A Because his mission was to shadow someone.

Q What do you call a secret agent on Christmas Day?

A A mince spy.

Q Why did the spy need insect spray?

A She learned her room was bugged.

1. Think of any number in the world.
2. Now double it.
3. Add 10 to the result.
4. Split the number in half.
5. Subtract your original number.

Your final answer is 5!

The M.I. High agents silently approached an abandoned factory on the outskirts of London. Rose peered through a dirty window in a door marked **KEEP OUT.**

"I see the Prime Minister and the Grand Master," she whispered.

Carrie could hardly believe what they were about to do. "Rescuing the Prime Minister and arresting the Grand Master for kidnapping ..." she marvelled. "This is going to be a great day!"

Just then, they heard someone skittering up next to them. "Thought I'd join you for this one," Chief Agent Stark informed them with his usual sneer.

"And steal the credit," Oscar muttered to Rose.

CRASH!

The agents burst through the door, startling the occupants inside.

"Grab the Grand Master ... I'll protect the PM!" barked Stark, throwing his arms around the startled politician. "Don't worry, Prime Minister. You're safe now," gasped Stark.

"You idiot, I *am* safe. We're signing a peace treaty!" the PM growled, breaking free.

"WHAT?" the agents cried in disbelief.

The Grand Master tried his best to look innocent behind his mask. "It's true. As of now, S.K.U.L. is no longer a criminal organisation. I'm going legit."

"And the Grand Master is receiving a full pardon," the PM added.

"You can't just let him off," argued Rose. "What about all the terrible things he's done?"

"I've made my decision," the PM said firmly. "As of now, the Grand Master is a free man. Now let him go, and that's an order!"

Later, at M.I. High HQ, Oscar guessed that the Prime Minister hoped the reduction of crime in Britain would help him get more votes in the upcoming election.

"If so, he made a grave error," Frank told them, switching on the TV. "This just aired."

Onscreen, the Grand Master was being interviewed by a news presenter. "I want to make our country a better place," he was saying. "And that's why I've decided to stand in this election for Prime Minister as a member of the S.K.U.L party!"

The agents' mouths dropped open in shock.

"I plan to disband the nation's security services. If the people of Britain trust in me, then I'll trust in them not to break the law," he proclaimed.

Immediately afterward, Stark summoned the team to his office at M.I.9 for an emergency assignment.

"The Grand Master is clearly planning to cheat, and your job is to find out how. Get me some dirt on him so we can throw him in jail!" Stark told them.

"We can't investigate a legitimate political party just because you don't want them to win," Frank objected. "That's morally wrong."

"Frank, this is the *Grand Master* we're talking about," Oscar protested.

"We can't let S.K.U.L. take over the country," agreed Rose.

Frank shook his head. "In a free country, the Secret Service doesn't choose the government. The Grand Master was pardoned, so he has the same rights as anyone else. I'll have no part of it." He walked out, leaving his agents stunned.

But Stark didn't seem to care. **"Find me something,"** he ordered the three spies. **"We're going to stop S.K.U.L. and I don't care how!"**

Soon, the agents had their chance. At a S.K.U.L. campaign stop, Oscar overheard the Grand Master making plans to meet his thugs behind the Bank of England that night. Clearly, he was going to rob it! The team had a newspaper journalist meet them there, then they burst inside.

"What a nice surprise," purred the Grand Master, handing a gigantic cheque over to a smiling little boy. He was donating £10,000 to a charity for orphans! The journalist quickly snapped a picture as Rose, Carrie and Oscar stood by, feeling foolish.

"I don't normally like publicity when I'm being wonderfully generous," the Grand Master told the journalist. "But since you're here, you may as well write about my many charitable works."

"We've been set up," Oscar groaned.

The next day, the photograph was on the front page of every newspaper, along with an article about M.I.9's failed attempt to sabotage S.K.U.L.'s campaign. Stark was furious at the agents' mistake.

"He's not going to win anyway," Carrie pointed out.

"Is that so?" Stark sneered. He switched on the news, which reported both parties were nearly equal in the polls. "My next move will ensure that the Grand Master loses the election," Stark went on. "But this time, I'm giving the job to real *adult* agents. Now trot off to nursery!"

Back at St Hope's, the agents found that even the school was fiercely divided over the PM election, with Mrs King and Mr Flatley competing to see who could wear the most campaign rosettes!

After classes were over, Rose, Oscar and Carrie met at HQ. They realised that Frank was right. It wasn't M.I.9's duty to choose the next Prime Minister – that right was given only to the people of Britain. And they would do whatever they could to protect that right, even if it meant stopping Agent Stark's plan.

Just then, Frank stepped out from where he had been listening. "I'm proud of you, agents," he said, and offered to help.

"But we haven't a clue how Stark is going to sabotage S.K.U.L.'s campaign," said Carrie.

"M.I.9 have been working on a weapon called an Oppositron Collider," Frank told them. "If you're hit with the beam, you say the exact opposite of what you intended."

Rose understood immediately. "Stark is going to use it on the Grand Master during the televised debates tonight. **Let's go!**"

But at the debates, everything went terribly wrong. The M.I. High team weren't fast enough to stop Stark's agent from using the Oppositron Collider, but they did manage to block the Grand Master from the beam. Instead, it hit Stark! Under the Prime Minister's questioning, he confessed his sabotage plans to all of Britain. With M.I.9 in complete disgrace, the Grand Master won the election by a landslide.

In despair, the agents watched the new Prime Minister's acceptance speech as it was broadcast from outside 10 Downing Street.

"The behaviour of the British security services during this election has shown exactly why we must shut them down," declared the Grand Master as he cuddled

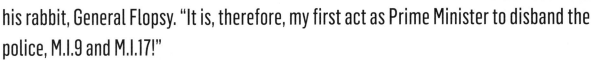

his rabbit, General Flopsy. "It is, therefore, my first act as Prime Minister to disband the police, M.I.9 and M.I.17!"

The team stared at each other in horror. They were no longer agents of M.I.9. There *was* no more M.I.9!

"... Oh, and one more thing," the Grand Master added. "General Flopsy is now Minister of Agriculture. Good night!"

With no police force or security service to protect the nation, a huge crimewave instantly swept through Britain. Robbers emptied shops and banks, and no one stopped them. The ex-agents met at HQ one last time to help Frank pack up the computers and his many gadgets.

"I can't believe it's over," said Rose sadly.

Oscar shook his head. "M.I.9 disbanded, along with the police and M.I.17 ..."

At that, the agents exchanged puzzled glances.

"Frank, what's M.I.17?" Carrie asked.

"It's just a small service that guards the nation's gold in the Treasury," he replied.

Suddenly, it all made sense to Rose. "That's it! That's the real reason the Grand Master got rid of security. He's planning to rob the Treasury!" she cried.

Oscar looked glum. "But we can't stop him. We're not agents anymore."

"Technically, M.I.9 exists until midnight tonight. So ..." Frank looked at them expectantly, waiting.

"One last time?" Rose asked her teammates, a smile spreading across her face.

Oscar and Carrie grinned back. ***"Let's do it!"***

At the Treasury, the agents didn't have to wait long.

SMASH!

A large part of the wall collapsed, and the Grand Master stepped through the hole into the vault. But aside from the teen agents, the Treasury was completely empty.

"What have you done with my gold?" the Grand Master shouted at the three spies.

"It looks like someone else stole it already," Oscar observed.

"With no police, people are nicking things before you can take it," Carrie laughed.

"First the Crown Jewels, then the diamond reserve and now this. Things haven't gone exactly as planned," the Grand Master admitted. "If I can get on television, I can order the police and security back to work immediately."

"We'll help you do that right now, if you resign as Prime Minister!" Rose told him.

The Grand Master agreed, and the team set up a television camera outside his office at 10 Downing Street.

"Hang on. How do we know you'll really resign?" Oscar asked him suspiciously.

"Because I never wanted to be PM in the first place. I just needed the power to shut down the security services so I could commit more crimes. I *assumed* you worked that out already," the Grand Master scoffed sarcastically.

"Just wanted to be sure," Oscar smiled.

But the agents knew that the Grand Master never kept his word. On his live broadcast to the nation, he reinstated the police and security, but said he would remain as Prime Minister! Luckily, Oscar had seen that coming. He cut to the video he had secretly recorded moments before, playing the Grand Master's incriminating confession to all of Britain.

Back on live TV, the Grand Master said nervously. "Er, under the circumstances ... I resign." And in a swirl of smoke, he legged it into the building!

Carrie, Rose and Oscar chased the villain through the corridors of 10 Downing Street. Just as they caught him and were about to remove his mask, the former PM rushed in and stopped them.

"I can't let you do that," he told them. "He hasn't done anything illegal since I pardoned him. And if this country stands for anything, it is equal justice," said the ex-PM.

Realising he was right, the agents released the Grand Master and watched him go.

"But he's going to commit loads of crimes. That's what he does," said Rose.

"Then we'll catch him," Carrie said brightly.

"Because that's what *we* do," finished Oscar.

"Maybe he'll leave his wicked ways behind," said the ex-PM optimistically. He felt around in his trouser pockets. "Wait a second. My wallet's gone! He took it!"

Frank grinned at his agents. "Business as usual."

THE END!

WICKED WORDSEARCH

Can you find these twelve words hidden in the square?
They can be read in any direction!

AGENTS ☐   FRANK ☐   ROSE ☐

CARRIE ☐   GRAND MASTER ☐   SECRET ☐

CLASSIFIED ☐   MI HIGH ☐   SKUL ☐

FLOPSY ☐   OSCAR ☐   SPIES ☐

H	J	F	F	L	O	P	S	Y	D	K	G
C	P	I	D	A	Q	V	M	P	L	C	P
L	W	S	E	C	R	E	T	B	I	W	J
A	B	K	Z	D	A	K	V	U	R	E	E
S	T	N	E	G	A	E	M	B	H	T	S
S	M	V	H	R	I	C	I	F	G	F	O
I	A	L	T	O	R	H	Y	R	O	V	R
F	O	U	P	A	K	G	J	A	R	S	X
I	Q	K	C	R	L	I	D	N	W	A	B
E	V	S	Z	G	P	H	K	K	D	M	C
D	O	C	L	Y	S	I	E	Q	D	U	S
G	R	E	T	S	A	M	D	N	A	R	G

SUPER SPIES

Real-life spies have sometimes changed the course of history, thanks to their daring work. Here are a few people that have become spy legends ...

British Flag

Roald Dahl

Before he became famous for writing children's books, Roald Dahl was a spy for M.I.6, the British military intelligence service during World War II. He started as a fighter pilot for the Royal Air Force, and was later stationed in the United States. There, he collected valuable information, or 'intelligence', and sent it back to M.I.6 for analysis.

Netherlands Flag   **French Flag**   **German flag**

Mata Hari

Born Margaretha Zelle in the Netherlands, Mata Hari was a dancer who often travelled between France and Germany during World War II. France learned that a spy with the codename H-21 was passing French secrets to Germany, and they accused Mata Hari of the crime. Britain also suspected her of being a German spy, but though neither country had any evidence, she was found guilty of espionage by French authorities.

Russian Flag   **German flag**   **French flag**

Edward Yeo-Thomas

Codenamed 'The White Rabbit', Edward Yeo-Thomas made many daring escapes as a British spy from behind enemy lines, including fighting his way out of a Russian prison during World War I. He then parachuted into German-occupied France and hid from capture in a hearse during World War II. Though he was eventually captured by Germans and sent to numerous prison camps, he managed to escape once again. His final act of heroism was to help bring several Nazi war criminals to trial after the war.

AGENT PROFILE

CONFIDENTIAL

ROSE GUPTA

AGE: 16

PROFILE: Rose is the team's resident genius. She's a scientific and technical expert with excellent analytical and research skills, and is often the one to work out clues during tricky missions. As the longest-serving member of M.I. High, she's always ready to take charge! She and Frank have a friendly rivalry going as they both love creating high-tech spy gadgets.

STRENGTH: Over the years, Rose has grown into her role as an M.I.9 agent. She's now confident in her skills and leadership abilities, and isn't afraid to speak up when she has an opinion.

M.I.9 AGENT

FEMALE
SURNAME: GUPTA
EYES: BROWN
HAIR: BLACK

ROSE

0011010101001011-1

WEAKNESS: Rose is a bit of a perfectionist in all matters, especially schoolwork and spy research. She used to dislike being called a nerd by other pupils, but now she's proud of it!

TOP SECRET TIP: At the start of the M.I. High programme, Rose had some trouble fitting in with her fellow agents, Blane and Daisy. She's much closer with Oscar and Carrie, and considers them her most trusted friends.

St Hope's High School

Rose Gupta

Age: 16

Year: 11

Form Teacher: Mr Flatley

048606

SPY SUDOKU

Take Rose's sudoku challenge! Each big grid contains four mini-grids in different colours. These mini-grids must include the numbers 1 to 4 in any order, but they can only appear once in each row and column of the big grid.

Work out the numbers that belong in the blank spaces.

A

1	2	3	
4		2	1
3	1		2
	4		3

B

	2	3	
1			2
3			4
	4	1	

ALERT!
This one's tougher!

CODE BREAKER

Oscar is in hiding from a S.K.U.L. agent! He has sent a message to Rose with his whereabouts in the school. Can you help crack his code and discover his location?

Code:

Fill in the alphabet backwards here:

A	B	C	D	E	F	G	H	I	J	K	L	M
Z												

N	O	P	Q	R	S	T	U	V	W	X	Y	Z
M												

R	'	N		R	M		G	S	V
	'								

H	X	R	V	M	X	V		O	Z	Y	.
											.

SPOT THE DIFFERENCE

These pictures look the same, but 8 things are different in picture 2.
Use your spy skills to spot them all!

Tick a box as you find each one.

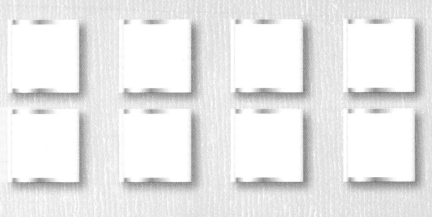

ROSE'S MISSION

Create your own hilarious spy mission! **Without reading the story first**, fill in the blue blanks with any words you like, as long as they fit the descriptions – the sillier the words, the better! Then read the story with your new words. You can also try it with a friend – one person can read out the descriptions, and the other can think of words. Read the story together, then switch tasks and do it again!

Quick tips:

Noun – a person, place or thing, like *book* or *circus*. A plural noun means more than one, like *cars*.

Adjective – a word that describes something, like *red* or *bouncy*.

Verb – an action word, like *swim* or *giggle*.

Exclamation – a word or sound that you shout out, like *'Oops!'* or *'Hey!'*

One day, Mr Flatley announced that a student from _____ would be
COUNTRY

visiting St. Hope's for _____ days.
NUMBER

"Would anyone like to volunteer to show _____ around the school?" he asked.
MALE NAME

"It would be good for him to learn how we _____ and _____ at St. Hope's."
VERB   VERB

Rose immediately said _____ . She couldn't wait to _____ the new
EXCLAMATION   VERB

student – would he be _____ , or would he be _____ ?
ADJECTIVE   ADJECTIVE

Suddenly, her _____ started _____ . Frank must have a new
NOUN   VERB ENDING IN -ING

_____ for her!
NOUN

"We have reason to believe the student is a S.K.U.L _____ ," he told Rose as
PROFESSION

he handed her a _____ . "Stay close and watch his every move. This gadget
NOUN

is an X-ray that may help you."

When the student arrived, Rose kept a close eye on him. She would _____
VERB

around corners and watch from behind _____ , hoping to catch him doing
PLURAL NOUN

something _____ , but he never did. By the last day of his visit, she
          ADJECTIVE

reckoned that Frank must have been wrong about him. As she said goodbye, she

noticed something very _____ about his _____ .
                 ADJECTIVE   ARTICLE OF CLOTHING

She used Frank's X-ray and realised the student was hiding a _____ !
                                           NOUN

"So you found out my secret," sneered the student. "But you're too late! I've already

discovered your spy headquarters under the school. Soon, S.K.U.L will _____
                                                VERB

St. Hope's and everyone with it!"

Out of nowhere, Frank appeared with a cool-looking _____ . He aimed it at the
                                          NOUN

villain and it flashed bright _____ . The S.K.U.L. agent looked _____
                         COLOUR   ADJECTIVE

and confused. "Where am I?" he asked. "Who am I?" Frank had used his _____
                                                  ADJECTIVE

gadget to _____ the baddie's memory!
          VERB

"Very_____ work," Frank said to Rose. She smiled as the S.K.U.L. agent
         ADJECTIVE

was taken away. St. Hope's School was safe and _____ – for now!
                                         ADJECTIVE

Smart spies write messages in code or invisible ink so that enemies won't be able to read it. But make sure your fellow spy knows which method you're using!

◎ Disguise the letters using a special key. You can assign different letters to the alphabet (as shown on page 33), have symbols instead of letters, use only the first or last letter of decoy words, or scramble the letters in a specific way. Use the Encrypter on page 47 for a hack-proof way of hiding your message.

◎ To use invisible ink, write your message on a sheet of plain paper with lemon juice and a thin paintbrush. The juice will dry clear, leaving no marks. Your fellow spy can slowly wave the paper over a lit light bulb to heat up the ink and reveal your message. Don't hold it too close or for too long or you'll burn your fingers!

Try cracking these codes!

Write only the first letter of each decoy word in the space below.

Yes, Oliver understands all red eagles behave erratically in nesting grounds.
Where are the caves he explores daily?

Hold this book up to a mirror to read the next message:

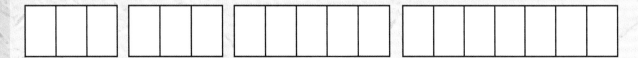

Answers: Decoy code - You are being watched. Mirror code - Meet me at the cinema at noon.

39

PENCIL COMMUNICATOR

This agent-to-agent communication device is used for nearly every mission. When Frank needs the team, he activates the beacon in the pencil's rubber to secretly summon them to HQ, and its clever disguise means that Mrs King won't confiscate it. Carrie, Oscar and Rose have invented a million excuses to leave the classroom when their communicators go off – from needing the toilet to finding a woggle!

SPY POD

M.I.9 created this valuable gadget to be an all-in-one tracking and surveillance tool for the M.I. High team. Its sleek, compact design conceals many functions, including video communication, infrared scanning, voice amplification, night vision technology, heartbeat detection and satellite navigation. Frank is constantly upgrading the Spy Pod with even more useful technology.

THE MOLE MACHINE

This giant tunnelling vehicle was invented by the arch criminal, the Mole, and his sidekick, Luke Withers. With the Mole in prison, Withers continued using the Mole Machine to tunnel into dozens of bank vaults and rob them. After the M.I. High agents arrested Withers, they kept the Mole Machine in storage at HQ. Later, the team had the perfect excuse to use it when they needed to bust Frank out of M.I.9 headquarters where he was being unfairly held and tickle-tortured!

M.I.9
SECRET SERVICE

ENEMY FILE

SUPER KRIMINAL
UNDERGROUND LEAGUE (S.K.U.L.)

PROFILE: Led by the mysterious criminal mastermind, the Grand Master, the evil members of S.K.U.L. have made countless attempts to destroy Britain's national security and eventually take over the world. Efforts to capture the Grand Master have been unsuccessful to date.

S.K.U.L. is a well-organised enemy operation, with its own training academy and access to advanced weapons. Previous failed diabolical schemes include introducing a new Ice Age, resurrecting a 2,000-year-old biological superweapon, blowing up the moon and unleashing an army of robotic animals at St Hope's School to expose M.I. High and put its agents in extreme danger!

TOP SECRET TIP: The Grand Master has only one companion that he truly trusts — an albino rabbit named General Flopsy. No one else in S.K.U.L. can measure up to his furry friend!

S.K.U.L. SWARM

How many S.K.U.L. logos are in the picture?
Count them all!

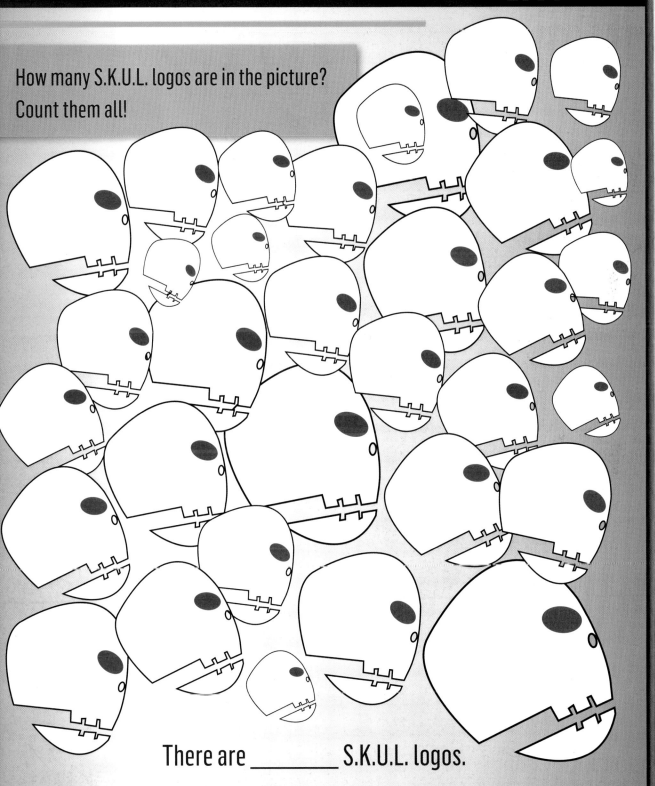

There are _____ S.K.U.L. logos.

Answer: There are 33 S.K.U.L. logos in the picture.

AGENT PROFILE ||||

CONFIDENTIAL

OSCAR COLE

AGE: 16

PROFILE: Oscar is a master of disguise, able to slip into any situation with his specialised skills for deep-cover operations. When it comes to impersonating someone, Oscar becomes a human chameleon and dives into his role 100 per cent! He even carries this into his everyday life at school by acting dull and slow-witted — a complete opposite of the real Oscar.

STRENGTH: Besides being highly intelligent, Oscar has many skills to help him go undercover — he can speak 14 languages and has extensive knowledge of spycraft and past M.I.9 missions.

M.I.9 AGENT

MALE
SURNAME: COLE
EYES: GREY/GREEN
HAIR: BLONDE

OSCAR

1110010010111100-01

WEAKNESS: Being a team player doesn't come easily to Oscar. With his father missing for years and his mother a double agent for S.K.U.L., Oscar found it hard to form close bonds with anybody. Now he thinks of Frank, Carrie and Rose as his family, but he'll always be a loner at heart.

TOP SECRET TIP: When Oscar's mother, Jade Dixon-Halliday, claimed to have left S.K.U.L. and wanted to return to M.I.9, Oscar was the only one who didn't believe her. He disobeyed orders to prove that she was a fraud — even though it meant turning against his own mum!

St Hope's High School

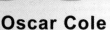

Oscar Cole

Age: 16

Year: 11

Form Teacher: Mr Flatley

046394

As an undercover expert, Oscar uses many false names.
Can you come up with a good alias? Here's a trick to help!

First name: Take the first name of your favourite celebrity or sports hero.

Middle name: Choose either the name of your pet or street.

Surname: Pick a letter from your postcode to find your new surname.

Abersmooshie	Jellibrain	Snufflebit
Bishbashbosh	Krashbang	Tippletoe
Crimblefur	Limburger	Uhhhh
Darkpants	Malarkey	Veruca
Eggles	Nooderoo	Wallbanger
Flump	Oleo	Xaardvark
Gargler	Periwinkle	Yeehaw
Herryknuckles	Quockenflur	Zingleberry
Impish	Radicchio	

MY SECRET AGENT ALIAS IS

THE ENCRYPTER

Create Encrypters for you and a friend! Cut out these wheels, then punch a hole in the centres. Place a red wheel over a blue one and use a split pin to fasten them together, making sure they can turn freely. Make both Encrypters, then give one to a friend.

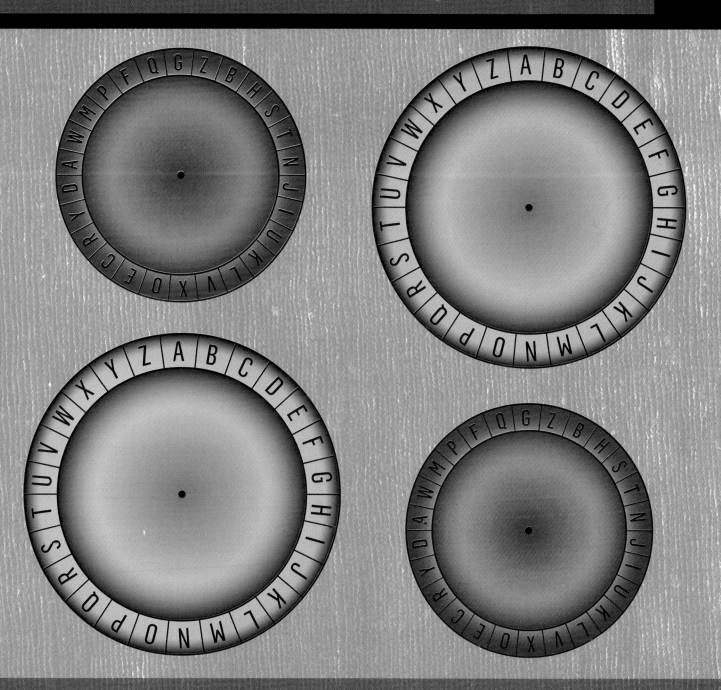

To encrypt your message, line up two different letters together on the wheels. Begin your message with a two-letter combination that will tell your fellow spy how to line up their wheel just like yours – AG or AY, for example. Then encrypt your message and give it to your friend to decipher. It can *only* be read by someone that has another Encrypter!

Oscar, Carrie and Rose each bring their special skills and unique personalities to form Britain's most awesome spy team. Which agent are you most like? Answer these questions to find out!

1

After school, you'll most likely be found:
a) Heading a Science Club meeting
b) Rehearsing a role for the school play
c) Working out at the gym

2

Which describes you best?
a) Brainiac
b) Lone wolf
c) Class clown

3

You'd love to be an M.I.9 agent because:
a) You'll get to work with high-tech spy gadgets
b) You'll be saving the world on a regular basis
c) You get to kick butt and it's totally legal!

4

What do you want to be when you grow up?
a) A multi-millionaire inventor
b) A spy, of course
c) An Olympic athlete

5

What's your favourite kind of music?
a) Classical
b) Rock
c) Pop

Mostly a's:
Supersmart, creative and mature beyond your years, you're a lot like Rose.

Mostly b's:
Intense and mysterious, you take your responsibilities seriously but work better on your own, just like Oscar.

Mostly c's:
Always cracking jokes and looking on the bright side of things, you've got loads of energy like Carrie.

SUNDAY EVENING.

KABOOM

PHEW, THAT WAS A *CLOSE* ONE!

AGENT CARRIE STEWART, MI9: SUPERIOR PHYSICAL SKILLS AND COMBAT PROWESS.

AGENT OSCAR COLE, MI9: MASTER OF DISGUISE, WORKS UNDERCOVER AND FLUENT IN 14 LANGUAGES.

AGENT ROSE GUPTA, MI9: SCIENTIFIC, TECHNICAL AND ANALYTICAL EXPERT WITH FORMIDABLE IQ RATING.

GOOD WORK, TEAM! THANKS TO YOU, THE *SKUL ROCKET* EXPLODED HARMLESSLY IN THE UPPER ATMOSPHERE – IT'S NOTHING BUT *SPACE DUST* NOW.

YOU'VE SAVED *HER MAJESTY'S* GALA CELEBRATIONS.

SPY MASTER FRANK LONDON, MI9: GIFTED AND ECCENTRIC SUPERVISOR OF MI9'S YOUNGEST RECRUITS.

NO THANKS NECESSARY, FRANK...

IT'S JUST WHAT WE *DO!*

M.I.HIGH IN NO FUTURE

● Agent Rik Hoskin, Licensed to Write ● Agent Will Sliney, Licensed to Illustrate ● Agent Phil Elliott, Licensed to Colour
● Agent Jimmy Betancourt, Licensed to Letter ● Special Agent Hannah Tibbetts, Incensed to Edit

ANY QUESTIONS?

CAREERS ADVICE-ADVICE, BABY! SCOOP DOGGY IS DOWN WIT DAT!

...MISTER WESLEY.

GOOD MORNING, STUDENTS OF *ST HOPE'S*. THE OPPORTUNITIES ARE *INFINITE* – I CAN'T WAIT TO DIRECT YOU TO YOUR *IDEAL CAREER PATH*.

SURE, GOOD LUCK WITH *THAT!*

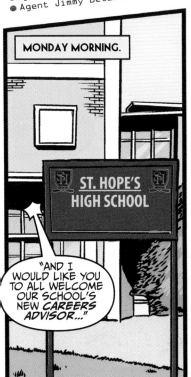

MONDAY MORNING.

ST. HOPE'S HIGH SCHOOL

"AND I WOULD LIKE YOU TO ALL WELCOME OUR SCHOOL'S NEW *CAREERS ADVISOR*..."

HAH, THANK YOU, YOUNG MAN. NO ONE CAN DOUBT YOUR *ENTHUSIASM!*

START

FINISH

SKUL

The teen agents are uncovering hidden clues to find the Grandmaster's secret lair. Lead them through the maze to the Grandmaster, picking up all four envelopes along the way.

DOSSIER LEVEL: CLASSIFIED

MR FLATLEY

PROFILE: Mr Flatley is the Head Teacher at St Hope's High School. Under his direction, the school has consistently come in very, very low in national rankings. His bumbling, easygoing nature encourages everyone to walk all over him, especially Mrs King.

STRENGTH: Hardworking and cheerful, Mr Flatley can be stubborn and determined when he feels strongly about something, such as his belief that St Hope's will be a top school one day, despite no evidence of this.

WEAKNESS: Mr Flatley is disorganised, absent-minded and oblivious to the school's problems, but this allows the M.I. High programme to operate without fear of detection. He's also secretly terrified of Mrs King.

THREAT LEVEL: None whatsoever. At all. Zero.

TOP SECRET TIP: His many weird hobbies include playing the accordion, Morris dancing, taking caravan trips and listening to Boldovian folk music.

MRS KING

PROFILE: Mrs King is deputy head teacher at St Hope's School. She is ambitious and has tried many times to have Mr Flatley sacked so she can take his place. She is devoted to the students, but thinks they would do better with strict discipline!

STRENGTH: Mrs King is extremely clever. She once discovered the M.I. High HQ but the spies then wiped her memory. When the wipe began to fail, Mrs King believed she was an M.I.9 agent and even caught a S.K.U.L. agent at St Hope's! The real spies hatched a plan to make her think her agent adventure was all just a dream.

WEAKNESS: She can be very bossy, especially when telling Mr Flatley how to run the school.

THREAT LEVEL: Medium. But if she becomes Head Teacher, the threat level will go up to HIGH!

TOP SECRET TIP: Though she's no fan of Mr Flatley, Mrs King had an embarrassingly massive crush on his brother Dave.

CONFIDENTIAL

Read the clues below and write the answers in the grid.

ACROSS

1. This spy is the longest-serving member of M.I. High.
2. We've never seen his face, but we probably don't want to, either.
3. She knows her geography from attending so many gymnastics meets.
4. He invents lots of ace gadgets for the teen spies.

DOWN

1. M.I.9 headquarters is in this city, and it's also Frank's surname.
2. He considers M.I. High his family, since he's never really had one.
3. This agent is secretly a whingey scaredy-cat.
4. This furry fiend isn't much of a talker.

Now unscramble the letters in the blue boxes to reveal the name of the person that S.K.U.L. is planning to kidnap!

To be an ace spy, you must have sharp eyes and a keen memory. Test your powers of observation by taking this test!

Look at this scene for exactly ten seconds. Try to remember every little detail you can. Then turn the page and answer the questions. Don't peek back at this picture unless you're really stuck!

EYE-Q TEST

Answer these questions by studying the scene on the previous page for exactly 10 seconds. How many did you get right?

1

Question 1
What colour is Rose's jumper?

2

Question 2
Which of the M.I. High agents is not wearing a backpack?

3

Question 3
Is Rose wearing a hat?

4

Question 4
Is Oscar's hair wavy or straight?

5

Question 5
What colour is Mrs King's suit?

6

Question 6
What is Carrie wearing on her wrists?

Answers: 1 - red, 2 - Carrie, 3 - no, 4 - wavy, 5 - blue, 6 - wrist sweatbands.

DARING DISGUISES

When infiltrating enemy territories, it's important that you don't get caught! The best way is to use a good disguise. Your face, clothes and even the way you walk are all easily changed. Here are some tips to get you started.

- Look in fancy dress shops for makeup, wigs, fake moustaches or beards to hide your face. 'Knock out' some teeth by sticking small squares of wet black paper on your front teeth to hide them. Glasses with non-prescription lenses are excellent for giving you a whole new look!

- Visit charity shops or borrow clothes in a completely different style than you usually wear. Going up a size and wearing a belt can transform your shape. Try wearing a memorable accessory like an arm sling, eyepatch or a plaster on your face so an enemy won't recognise you if he sees you without it later.

- Personal habits can give away even the best disguise. Change your stride – practice shuffling, swinging your arms or limping. Using gestures when talking, speaking in a deeper or higher voice, or changing your posture are also good ways to go undercover.

Put together a complete disguise, then test it out on your family or friends.

STUDENT PROFILES

SCOOP DOGGY

PROFILE: St Hope's student Scoopy Doggy is an aspiring rapper, although it's universally agreed that his rhyming skills are extremely poor. He often wears a full-length fur coat and hat, even in extreme heat. Scoop Doggy's real name is rumoured to be Timothy Hinklebottom.

TOP SECRET TIP: Scoop was recruited as an M.I. High agent with the aid of Smart-Ease, a tonic that accelerates agent training. He proved to be very clever and excelled in his mission to defeat the Grandmistress. When the effects of the tonic receded, his memory of the mission was erased.

AVRIL FRANKLIN

PROFILE: The St Hope's school president, Avril is sensitive, intelligent and passionate about nearly every cause she comes across. Described by other students as an 'emo', 'non-conformist' and someone who 'cares too much about everything'.

TOP SECRET TIP: Avril has a huge crush on Oscar and is forever trying to learn more about him through strong interrogation tactics. She was recruited as an M.I. High agent, but her memory of the mission was later erased.

DAVINA BERRY

PROFILE: Besides being a St Hope's student, Davina desperately hopes to be a future WAG. She's convinced she will be rich and famous through one means or another, though there is no evidence of talent or intelligence to support that. She's always on her mobile, addicted to reality TV shows and is extremely vain. He best friend is Donovan Butler.

TOP SECRET TIP: Davina has an intense fear of folk music. She was recruited as an M.I. High agent but her memory of the mission was later erased.

DONOVAN BUTLER

PROFILE: St Hope's student Donovan Butler has set his sights on being a future premier footballer, as it seems to be an easy way to become insanely rich and famous. This brilliant idea will also help his best friend, Davina Berry, achieve her goal of being a WAG.

TOP SECRET TIP: Donovan has a deep phobia of corduroy clothing.

THE FINAL MISSION

Fancy yourself an expert on M.I. High? Test your spy skills with this grand-monstrous quiz!

1 Oscar's surname is:

A. Dixon
B. Halliday
C. Cole

2 What is Frank's undercover profession at St. Hope's School?

A. cook
B. caretaker
C. teacher

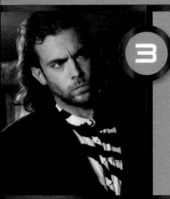

3 Carrie is ace at:

A. physical combat
B. languages
C. inventing gadgets

4 Who is the longest-serving spy at M.I. High?

A. Oscar
B. Carrie
C. Rose

5 In the story "Vote S.K.U.L.", the upcoming election was for which post?

A. Prime Minister
B. Defence Minister
C. Chief Agent of M.I.9

6 General Flopsy is a:

A. hedgehog
B. rabbit
C. naked mole rat

7 As part of her disguise as an ordinary student, Rose wears:

A. a wig
B. braces
C. glasses

8 Oscar's parents are:

A. spies
B. diplomats
C. police officers

9 Davina is best friends with:

A. Avril Franklin
B. Donovan Butler
C. Rose Gupta

10 St. Hope's School is known for its:

A. ace football team
B. award-winning architecture
C. low national ranking

11 Carrie's chief weakness is a fear of:

A. bad jokes
B. ghosts
C. folk music

12 In the comic "No Future", this device hypnotised the students.

A. The Spy Pod
B. The Despair Bomb
C. The Mind Drill

14 What is Scoop Doggy's real name?

A. Timothy Hinklebottom
B. Donovan Butler
C. Horatio Stark

15 Which of these children's book writers was a spy for Britain?

A. Enid Blyton
B. Roald Dahl
C. Lewis Carroll

15 The acronym S.K.U.L. stands for:

A. Super Krime Underwear League
B. Super Kriminal Underworld League
C. Sinister Kriminals Underground League

16 S.K.U.L. is headed by:

A. The Groove Master
B. The Grand Maestro
C. The Grand Master

Answers on page 68.

THE FINAL MISSION ANSWERS:

1 - C	7 - C	13 - A
2 - B	8 - A	14 - A
3 - A	9 - B	15 - B
4 - C	10 - C	16 - C
5 - A	11 - B	TOTAL:
6 - B	12 - C	

1-6: SLACKER SPY
Tragic! Head back to spy school for basic training.

7-11: SERIOUS SPY
Well done! You've got what it takes to be a good spy, but still have some work to do.

12-16: SUPER SPY
Congratulations, agent! You've successfully completed this tricky mission.

PENDRIX'S PUZZLE

ATTENTION AGENTS! Have you discovered and decrypted all the clues to Pendrix's puzzle on page 9? In the space below, write the secret location where he's hidden the Queen's corgis:

Hold this book up to a mirror to reveal the secret location: nobnoJtolworsdH

Answer: The code words are on pages: 10, 14, 17, 20, 25, 29, 32, 38, 40, 42, 46, 48 (twice), 59, 64, 67.

CALLING ALL AGENTS!

CONFIDENTIAL

M.I.HIGH
SCHOOL + SPY = M.I.HIGH

SKUL
SUPER KRIMINAL UNDERWORLD...

Read more fast-paced adventures from the team at M.I. High.

BOOK 2
BOOK 1

Coming soon, two brand new books so classified we can't show you ... yet!

On sale January 2012 £5.99
For more inside intel, sign up at
egmont.co.uk/MIhigh

©Kudos Film and Television Ltd 2011

E0955